C000089126

It's Another Ace Book from CGP

It's chock-full of questions that are carefully designed to make sure you know all the _really important stuff_ about 'Dissolving' in Year Six Science.

And we've had a really good stab at making it funny — so you'll actually _want to use it_.

Simple as that.

CGP are just the best

The central aim of Coordination Group Publications is to produce top quality books that are carefully written, beautifully presented and marvellously funny — whilst always making sure they exactly cover the National Curriculum for each subject.

And then we supply them to as many people as we possibly can, as _cheaply_ as we possibly can.

Buy our books — they're ace

Contents

Answers to the questions are on the back of the Pull-out Poster in the centre of the book.

Published by Coordination Group Publications Ltd.

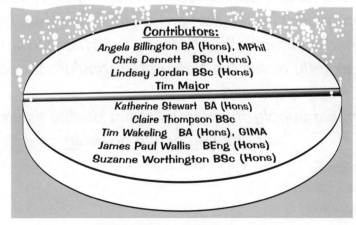

Contributors:

Angela Billington BA (Hons), MPhil
Chris Dennett   BSc (Hons)
Lindsay Jordan BSc (Hons)
Tim Major

Katherine Stewart BA (Hons)
Claire Thompson BSc
Tim Wakeling   BA (Hons), GIMA
James Paul Wallis   BEng (Hons)
Suzanne Worthington BSc (Hons)

ISBN 1-84146-275-6
Groovy website: www.cgpbooks.co.uk
Jolly bits of clipart from CorelDRAW
Printed by Elanders Hindson, Newcastle upon Tyne.

Background

You'll have done a bit about <u>dissolving</u> before, so you know that some things dissolve in water (groovy), some things just stay there (boring), and some things go all fizzy (glorious). OK, brace yourself — there's more to this dissolving business than you could shake a stick at...

Q1 Susan and Bob are making a huge, multi-flavoured soup. They don't know which of their ingredients will dissolve in the hot water, and which will just sink to the bottom and stay there. Write 'dissolves' or 'doesn't' under each ingredient.

SALT

PEPPER

CARROT

ARTIFICIAL SWEETENER

HAM

POTATOES

BANANA

For some reason, no one ever liked Susan and Bob's soup.

SUGAR CUBES

<u>Read on — your problems will dissolve...</u>

Lucky you if you find this page easy. But if you find it's trickier than dissolving a banana, <u>don't worry</u> — by the time you've <u>got</u> through this book, you'll be a <u>dissolving expert</u>.

Filtering

Two great ways to get solids out of water are <u>filtering</u> and <u>sieving</u>. You have to know what size the pieces of solid are to know which is the right method. You have to use your <u>noddle</u>...

Twins Sam and Tina have found a lovely, big, dirty puddle. They want to separate the water, stones and sand. They've thought up two methods each, but they can't agree on which will work best.

Sam

Tina

Q1 Look at these pictures and descriptions of the methods Sam and Tina suggested. Circle the the best method.

(A) Tina could pluck out the stones by hand, then filter the water to get the sand out.

(B) Sam could wait while the water settles completely. Then he'd carefully scoop the clean water from the top of the puddle.

(C) Tina could filter the water to get the stones and sand out.

(D) Sam could sieve the water to get the stones out, then filter it to remove the sand.

Q2 Write down why you chose the one you did.

....

....

Freddie was worried he'd get caught in the sieve if he didn't lose weight.

Q3 For each method you wouldn't use, write down its letter and why you wouldn't use it.

1. ....

2. ....

3. ....

This page is fil-ter bursting with great stuff...

Simple stuff this — and you've probably done it before anyway. Just remember, <u>big</u> comes first when it comes to separation. <u>Sieve</u> out the big then <u>filter</u> out the small — it's a piece of cake.

Filtering

Right, I'd bet money that you're just about ready for another page on <u>separating solids</u>.
And that's just what I've got here for you. So go on, get to it...

Jock likes biscuits in his hot chocolate, so he mashes them up.
He ends up with some powdery crumbs and some quite large pieces of biscuit.
As he spoons them into his cup he thinks he sees tiny bits of a spider.

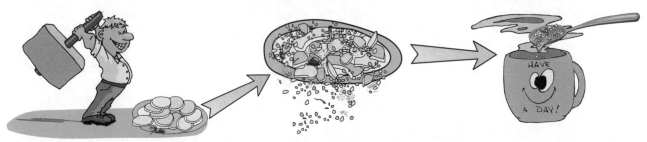

Q1   Jock wants to separate the larger pieces from his hot chocolate. Then he wants to separate the smaller bits (and the bits of spider) from the hot chocolate. Then he can put the big bits back, without any spider. How can he do it? (Clue: he needs to do 2 different things.)

1) ....
   ....

2) ....
   ....
   ....

Q2   Stealthy Laura the jewel thief almost got caught stealing diamonds and gold dust, so she hid them in a toilet water tank. She has crept back to get them. How can she separate them from the water?

Angus and Stacy loved biscuits and hot chocolate.

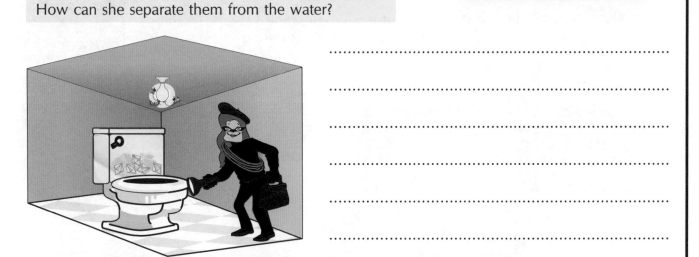

....
....
....
....
....
....

Is it filtering in yet?...

You're gonna be a pro at this soon — any time anybody needs solids separating from liquids they're gonna call on you. Big <u>then</u> little. Sieve <u>then</u> filter. Oh, so satisfyingly simple...

Filtering

OK, let's just get on with another page all about <u>filtering</u> and stuff.

Carrie is upset because her snotty little brother, Sid, has put loads of chalk dust in the tank with her fish. She's worried they will choke on it and die.

Q1 The different stages Carrie will have to go through to get the chalk dust out of the water are written on the right. Write them nice and small in the right order in this flow chart.

Rinse out any last traces of chalk dust from the fish tank. Collect the stones from the sieve and put them back in the tank.

Put the clean water back in the fish tank. Then add all the fish and plants.

Remove the plants and each fish with a net. Put them in a separate tank.

Pour the water into a funnel lined with filter paper, with a bucket underneath.

Pour all the stones, water and chalk dust out of the tank into a sieve, with a bucket underneath.

These little boxes are for Q2.

The fish tank set off to get revenge on Sid.

Q2 These pictures show parts of each of the five stages in Q1. Write the correct letter in the bottom right corner of each of the boxes above.

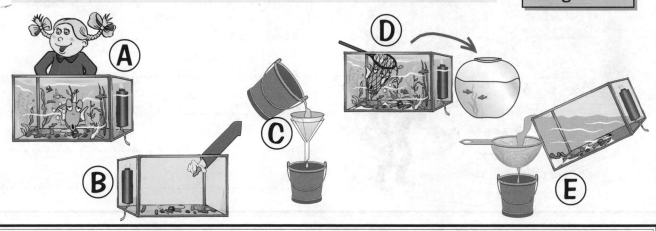

It doesn't take a mas-sieve effort to learn this...

At last, the end of the third page on filtering. Thank heavens — time for solutions... Whooppee.

Solutions — Dissolving

Once you've mixed a solid with water, separating it by filtering only works if the solid hasn't <u>dissolved</u> in the water. When a solid dissolves, it breaks down into <u>tiny pieces</u> which would fall <u>straight through</u> a piece of filter paper.

Maurice has five beakers of distilled water. He's left the first one alone, but put different solids into the other four.

Q1 Which beakers now contain pure water?

....

Q2 (Circle) the right words to finish off this sentence about solutions.

When a solid DISSOLVES / EXPLODES in water, it forms a SOLUTION /

PURE LIQUID that might be transparent or COLOURED / INVISIBLE .

Q3 Which of the things on the right could be mixed with water to make these solutions? Write the correct letters in the boxes underneath the solutions.

coffee	blue ink solution	filtered sea water
☐	☐	☐

Fred was too busy worrying about his loo roll running away to worry about dissolving.

Tired? — I've heard coffee's a good solution...

If a solid can <u>dissolve</u>, it means that when you put it in water it breaks down into <u>really tiny</u> pieces — much smaller than the holes in filter paper. That's why you <u>wouldn't</u> be able to filter it out.

Solutions — Evaporating

You can't filter out a solid once it's dissolved — you have to use another way to separate it from the liquid. That's if you want to, of course — I like my hot chocolate with the chocolate still in it.

Q1 What's the best way to get a solid back once it's dissolved in water? Tick the box next to the right answer.

Pour the solution through a sieve. ☐   Put the solution in the freezer. ☐

Leave it for a while so the water evaporates. ☐   Use filter paper. ☐

Give it a good shake. ☐   Coax it out with a tempting morsel of cheese. ☐

Lizzie's mum's given her a massive mug of tomato soup made from soup granules. Lizzie hates soup, but she knows that liquids can evaporate, so she reckons if she leaves it for a bit it'll **all disappear**.

Q2 After 2 weeks, the mug was almost empty except for a hard, dark red solid coating on the bottom. Did this result support Lizzie's prediction?

....

After 2 hours   After 2 weeks

Q3 Fill in the blanks in these sentences using words from the brackets.

When you leave a solution of a liquid and a solid for a long

time, only the .... (SOLID / LIQUID)

evaporates off. That means that when all the

.... (SOLID / LIQUID) has gone, there's

only the .... (SOLID / LIQUID) left.

Two years later, Lizzie realised she should have just poured the soup down the sink.

Don't be wet — learn about evaporating...

Peculiar stuff, science — if you want to separate a dissolved solid from a liquid, you just wait until the liquid <u>escapes</u> from the solid. That's pretty important — especially if you like dried soup.

Solutions — Filtering

Some solutions, like salty water or sugar solution, can <u>look</u> just like pure water. An easy-peasy way to tell if something can't be filtered out is to taste it afterwards. BUT make sure everything is <u>completely clean</u>, and ONLY TASTE THINGS THAT ARE SAFE TO DRINK.

Q1 Here are some dissolving experiments with some of the pictures missing.
Draw the missing bits in the spaces provided. For each experiment, tick one of the boxes to say whether the solid has been filtered out or is still in the solution.

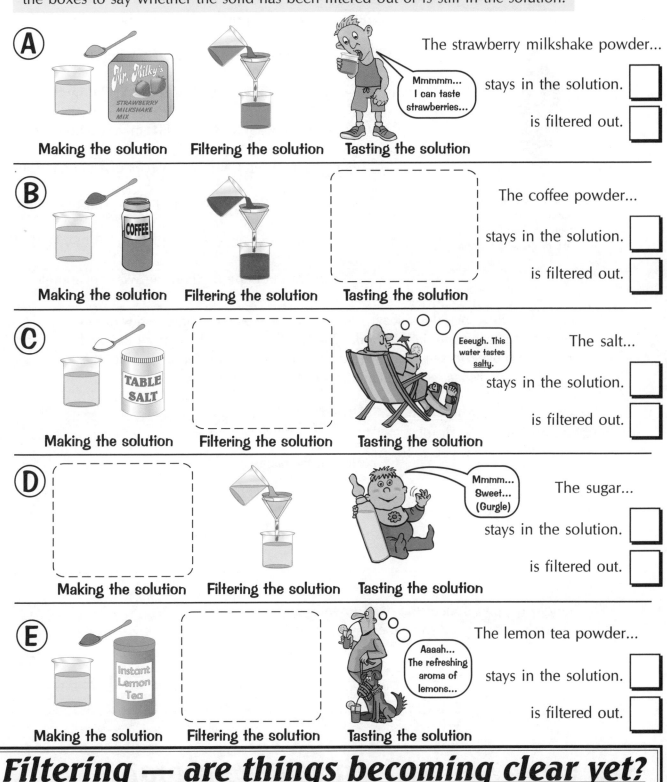

A Making the solution — Filtering the solution — Tasting the solution
Mmmmm... I can taste strawberries...
The strawberry milkshake powder...
stays in the solution. ☐
is filtered out. ☐

B Making the solution — Filtering the solution — Tasting the solution
The coffee powder...
stays in the solution. ☐
is filtered out. ☐

C Making the solution — Filtering the solution — Tasting the solution
Eeeugh. This water tastes <u>salty</u>.
The salt...
stays in the solution. ☐
is filtered out. ☐

D Making the solution — Filtering the solution — Tasting the solution
Mmmm... Sweet... (Gurgle)
The sugar...
stays in the solution. ☐
is filtered out. ☐

E Making the solution — Filtering the solution — Tasting the solution
Aaaah... The refreshing aroma of lemons...
The lemon tea powder...
stays in the solution. ☐
is filtered out. ☐

Filtering — are things becoming clear yet?

You can do these experiments yourself, either at home or at school. You don't have to stick to the things on this page — but <u>always</u> use stuff that's <u>safe to taste</u> at the end of the experiment.

More on Solutions

Here we go again — even more questions about what's really happening when solids seem to disappear and re-appear again. Remember, things don't disappear when they dissolve. They're still there, so if you evaporate the liquid off, you'll get the solid back.

Q1 (Circle) the right words to finish off this paragraph about evaporation.

And don't even THINK about turning over the page until you've done ALL of these questions.

When the water evaporates from a solution, the LIQUID / SOLID is left behind. This is because when the solid was put in the water, it DISSOLVED / EVAPORATED by breaking up into tiny pieces LARGER / SMALLER than the holes in a piece of filter paper. Water and tiny pieces of solid can form a SOLUTION / GAS together, but they're still two different things. The pieces of solid can't DISSOLVE / EVAPORATE , so they're left behind when the water evaporates.

Pippa had three big, flat dishes. She put distilled water in one, rain water in another and sea water in the third. She left them out in the sun all day and then came back to see what they looked like — but she forgot to label the dishes, so she didn't know which one was which.

Q2 Which one of the flat dishes in the bottom picture had distilled water* in it? How can you tell?

*If you're not sure what distilled water is, see the box at the bottom of the page.

....

....

....

Q3 What would happen if, after the experiment, Pippa poured water into dish A and gave it a stir?

....

....

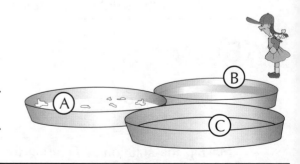

Sea water? — Yes, can you see it too?...

Distilled water is just water and nothing else — that's why it doesn't leave anything behind when it evaporates. It's made by heating water, collecting and cooling the steam to turn it back to a liquid.

Even More on Solutions

Nearly there — just a few more questions on solutions and you'll
be an <u>expert</u>. You'll be able to <u>amaze</u> your friends, or supply
them with huge stonking mountains of...er, sea salt.

Franny's been eating some boiled sweets,
but she doesn't like the orange ones.
For an experiment, she grinds them up and
dissolves the orange powder in a jar of
water, which she leaves on a hot radiator.

Q1 After a while, the jar has no liquid in it — an orange solid
is left on the bottom. What's happened to the water?

....

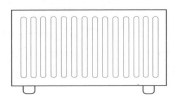

Now Franny's got three jars of cold
water and three powdered solids (she
doesn't know what they are). After
stirring the same amount of each
powder into different jars, Franny left
the jars to stand. After five minutes,
<u>none</u> of powder A could be seen at the
bottom of the jar, but <u>all</u> of powder **B**
and <u>some</u> of powder **C** could be seen.

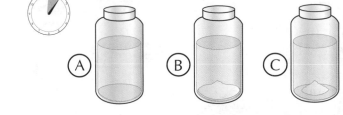

Q2 Could the powders put into jars A and B be the same material? Explain why or why not.

....

....

Q3 What about the powders put into jars B and C?

....

....

These questions are bound to cause a stir...

...but they're dead <u>useful</u>. Now you can call yourself a Master of Solutions.

Evaporating Water from Solutions

When you do something to water, like <u>boiling</u> it or <u>adding</u> stuff to it, think about whether or not you can change everything <u>back</u> to how it started.

Q1 Ellen is boiling some water and she notices that the water level goes down. Choose the sentence that explains where the water's going, and write it out underneath.

| The water leaks out of the bottom of the container. | The water gets squashed so it's smaller. | The water just disappears completely. | The water goes into the air as steam. |

....

....

Q2 Ellen added some sand and sugar to some water.

As soon as she'd done it, she changed her mind. She reckoned that she could separate the sand out again using the method on the right — so she tried it.

a) What's the process she used called?

....

b) Ellen thought she could separate the sugar out using a different method — this is what she did:

Draw in the important missing piece of equipment in the red box. Pick from the bits in the yellow box.

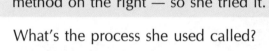

c) What is the name of the method she used in part b?

....

Q3 Was Ellen right when she thought that she could separate the sugar and sand out from the water again?

Sherlock found the solution to the mystery, but it was evaporating fast.

....

Unmake me a cup of coffee...

It's easy enough to separate things out from water, as long as they <u>haven't reacted</u>. You just have to remember the two main ways of separating things — <u>filtering</u> (or sieving) and <u>evaporating</u>.

Evaporating Water from Solutions

When you heat a mixture of water and a solid, not all the
different parts of the mixture evaporate.

Q1   Sandra the alien is heating up some purple ink
with her heat gun, and collecting and condensing
the steam. Will the condensed steam be purple?

....

Q2   Now Sandra is collecting steam by
heating up sugary water. Will the
condensed steam be sugary?

....

Q3 a) Sandra's getting quite confused now. This
time she's heating up water with dissolved tea
in it. Will the condensed steam taste of tea?

....

b) If not, why not? Where is the tea flavour?

....

....

Q4   Planet Zapf's top scientist has been given a jar of
condensed steam from each of Sandra's experiments.
The water in each jar is clear and doesn't taste of
anything. What does this prove?

....

....

....

....

Emperor Zplat was STILL
waiting for Sandra to bring
him his cup of tea.

Don't run out of steam — you haven't finished yet...

Now you've done this page, you should be all clear about which bits of a mixture can be evaporated
off. There's no point drinking the condensed steam from a cup of tea — it would just be hot water.

Evaporating Water from Solutions

Here's a surprise — all this stuff about evaporating could actually be <u>useful</u> in real life.

Q1   Carlton and Andy are stuck in a boat at sea, and
they need to make pure water from the salty sea
water. While Carlton was feeling sorry for himself,
Andy cobbled together this apparatus.

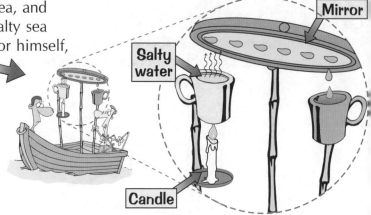

a)   Carlton thinks they should let the
boiling water in the yellow mug cool
down, and then drink it — but Andy
thinks they should drink the condensed
steam in the green mug. Who is right?

....

b)   How does Andy's invention work?

....

....

....

....

WARNING
Don't do this experiment — the water
might not be completely safe to drink.
This method is only good for emergencies.

c)   Carlton tried a bit of the water from the green mug, and he noticed that
it didn't taste salty. What does that prove? Circle the right answer.

Salt evaporates if	Only the water has	You can only
you heat it up.	evaporated — the salt	taste salt when
	was left behind.	it's cold.

Andy wasn't too happy
when Carlton said that he
would have preferred
orange juice.

d)   Fill in the blanks by using words from the brackets.

When you .... (EVAPORATE / FILTER) a

mixture of water and a dissolved solid, the steam only contains

.... (WATER / THE SOLID) and not

.... (WATER / THE SOLID).   That's because

only the .... (SALT / WATER) evaporates.

Remember this page if you're ever stuck at sea...

That's enough about evaporation for now. It's a pretty useful method, and it really does <u>work</u> if
you're desperate for clean(ish) water — but generally speaking, a tap is a lot easier and quicker...

KS2 Science Answers — More About Dissolving

Page 17 Graph City

Q1: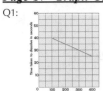

Q2: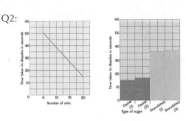

The graph should be easier to understand than the table of results.

(These graphs were drawn using the spare results.)

Page 18 Graph City

Q1:

Own results

Results from page 18

Say whether the results from page 18 (BLUE LINE) are similar to own results or not (answer depends on results).

Q2: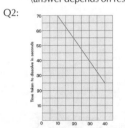

Q3: Yes — the hotter the water, the faster the sugar dissolves.

Q4: Use all of the ways to speed up dissolving — use lots of hot water, use caster sugar rather than granulated, and stir it a lot.

Q5: The most effective was raising the water temperature.
The least effective was increasing the volume of water.

Page 19 Repeating Experiments

Q1: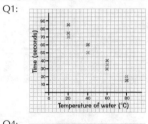

Q2: a) The results for 80 °C are close together.
b) The results for 20 °C are spread out.

Q3: a) You'd trust the results at 80 °C the most.
b) You'd trust the results at 20 °C the least.

Q4: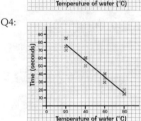

KEY: ✗ Louise

✗ Roger

✗ Hilary

Page 20 Drawing a Good Line on Your Graphs

Q1: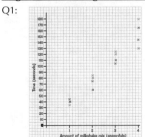

Key	
✗	Adam's results
✗	Alison's results
✗	Julie's results
✗	Rohan's results
	Average results

Page 21 Drawing a Good Line on Your Graphs

Q1: a) You should be able to trust the results with 1 teaspoon the most.
b) You would trust the results with 4 teaspoons the least.

Q2: These two should be ringed:
So there are roughly as many points above the line as below it, and
So that the slope of the line roughly shows the pattern of the results.

Q3: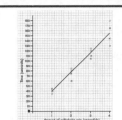

Q4: a)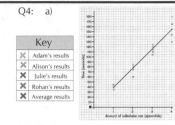

Key	
✗	Adam's results
✗	Alison's results
✗	Julie's results
✗	Rohan's results
✗	Average results

Q4: b) **'The average line is about the same as my line'** should be ringed.
c) YES
d) A correct answer should say that a larger amount of milkshake mix will take longer to dissolve.

Page 22 Making a Good Conclusion

Q1: Green Line — BAD — There are more points below the line than above the line.

Red Line — GOOD — There are the same number of points above and below the line

Blue Line — BAD — There are more points above the line than below the line.

Q2: The warmer the milk, the less time it takes for the milkshake mix to dissolve.

Q3: It's useful to repeat results because it proves that you weren't just lucky the first time you did the experiment. If all your results are similar, they're more likely to be right.

Page 23 Revision Questions

Q1: ✗ BANANA   ✗ POTATOES   ✔ SALT
✗ PEPPER   ✔ SUGAR CUBES

Q2: 1) Use a sieve to remove the gravel.
2) Separate the dust out of the water using filter paper and a funnel.

Q3: When you leave a solution of a liquid and a solid for a long time, only the **LIQUID** evaporates off. That means that when all the **LIQUID** has gone, there's only the **SOLID** left.

Q4: The coffee powder stays in the solution ✔   PICTURE:

Page 24 Revision Questions

Q1: When a solution is made, the solid is put into water and it **DISSOLVES** by breaking up into pieces **SMALLER** than the holes in a piece of **FILTER** paper. If you heat up the solution, the water evaporates, but the pieces of solid can't **EVAPORATE** so they're left behind. That means that the steam only contains **WATER** and not the **SOLID**.

Q2: The condensed steam won't be red, because it contains only water. All the red ink is left behind in the first dish (if all the water is evaporated off, there will only be a red solid left).

Q3:

Goes through highest points.   Goes through lowest points.   Goes through the middle.

BAD   BAD   GOOD

Page 25 Revision Questions

Q1:

Statement	True or False?	How could you test it?
If you evaporate sweetened tea, the sugar will evaporate with the water.	FALSE	Leave a cup of sweetened tea until most of the liquid has gone, then taste what's left over. It will taste a lot sweeter.
Salt will dissolve quicker in hot water than in cold water.	TRUE	Try stirring a teaspoonful of salt into a cup of hot water and one of cold water. The salt in the hot water will dissolve first.
Chalk will dissolve in water.	FALSE	Stir a spoonful of chalk dust into a beaker of water and filter the mixture with filter paper. The chalk will get caught in the filter and separate from the water.
It makes a difference whether you stir clockwise or anti-clockwise.	FALSE	Put the same amount of sugar into two identical beakers of water. Stir one clockwise and one anticlockwise. They should dissolve at the same rate.
Bath salts dissolve quicker when you stir the water.	TRUE	Put the same amount of bath salts into two identical beakers of water. Stir one and leave the other to stand. The bath salts being stirred will dissolve faster.

Q2: 1. FILTERING   2. SOLUTION   3. DISSOLVE
4. WATER   5. SAME   6. STEAM
7. FAIR

From the KS2 Science book M

KS2 Science Answers — *More About Dissolving*

Page 1 Background

Q1: SALT — dissolves   PEPPER — doesn't
CARROT — doesn't   ARTIFICIAL SWEETENER — dissolves
HAM — doesn't   POTATOES — doesn't
BANANA — doesn't   SUGAR CUBES — dissolves

Page 2 Filtering

Q1: D

Q2: The stones are big, so they can be sieved out. The pieces of sand are a lot smaller and would go straight through the sieve, so it's easiest to get them out by filtering.

Q3: 1. A — it would take too long to for Tina to pick all the stones out by hand.
2. B — Sam wouldn't be able to get all of the water out of the puddle.
3. C — The stones would block up the filter.

Page 3 Filtering

Q1: 1. Pour the tea through a sieve to collect the large bits of biscuit.
2. Filter the tea to remove the small bits and the pieces of spider, then replace the large bits caught in the sieve.

Q2: Sieve the water from the tank to remove the diamonds, then filter the water to separate it from the gold dust.

Page 4 Filtering

Q1: The correct order is: 1. Remove the plants and each fish with a net...
2. Pour out all the stones, water and chalk dust...
These two can be   3. Pour the water into a funnel...
the other way round.   4. Rinse out any last traces of chalk dust...*
5. Put the clean water back in the fish tank...

Q2: The correct order is: D, E, C*, B*, A

Page 5 Solutions — Dissolving

Q1: Only beaker number 1 contains pure water.

Q2: When a solid **DISSOLVES** in water, it forms a **SOLUTION** that might be transparent or **COLOURED**.

Q3: Coffee — E   Blue ink solution — D   Filtered sea water — B

Page 6 Solutions — Evaporating

Q1: ✔ Leave it for a while so the water evaporates.

Q2: There was still some solid left, so the result didn't support Lizzie's prediction.

Q3: When you leave a solution of a liquid and a solid for a long time, only the **LIQUID** evaporates off. That means that when all the **LIQUID** has gone, there's only the **SOLID** left.

Page 7 Solutions — Filtering

Q1: ✔ Stays in the solution (for all of the five solids).
PICTURES:

A:

B:

C:

D:

(or similar)

Page 8 More on Solutions

Q1: When the water evaporates from a solution, the **SOLID** is left behind. This is because when the solid was put in the water, it **DISSOLVED** by breaking up into tiny pieces **SMALLER** than the holes in a piece of filter paper. Water and tiny pieces of solid can form a **SOLUTION** together, but they're still two different things. The pieces of solid can't **EVAPORATE**, so they're left behind when the water evaporates.

Q2: C — the one with no solid left in it. Distilled water leaves no solid because nothing's dissolved in it.

Q3: The solid would dissolve and form a solution again.

Page 9 Even More on Solutions

Q1: The water's all evaporated.

Q2: The powders in jars A and B can't be the same material because one of them has dissolved completely but the other hasn't dissolved at all.

Q3: The powders in jars B and C can't be the same material because one of them hasn't dissolved at all but half of the other one has dissolved.

Page 10 Evaporating Water from Solutions

Q1: The water goes into the air as steam.

Q2: a) Filtering   b)
c) Evaporation

Page 11 Evaporating Water from Solutions

Q1: No, the condensed steam won't be purple.

Q2: No, the condensed steam won't be sugary.

Q3: a) The condensed steam won't taste of tea.
b) The tea flavour is left behind in the solid in the wide dish.

Q4: It proves that when a solution is heated up, only the water evaporates. All the solid is left behind.

Page 12 Evaporating Water from Solutions

Q1: a) Andy's right — they should drink the condensed steam.
b) When the sea water is heated, pure water evaporates off as steam and is condensed on the mirror. The liquid collected in the green mug is pure water. All the salt is left behind in the yellow mug.
c) Only the water has evaporated — the salt was left behind.
d) When you **EVAPORATE** a mixture of water and a dissolved solid, the steam only contains **WATER** and not **THE SOLID**. That's because only the **WATER** evaporates.

Page 13 Dissolving Faster

Q1: ✔ A fair test is when only one thing gets changed...

Q2: These things could affect how quickly sugar dissolves:
How much sugar there is in the water.
Whether you use fine or coarse sugar.
How many times you stir the sugar, and how vigorously.
How much water there is.
What temperature the water is.

Page 14 Water Volume and Dissolving

Q1: ✔ Use exactly one flat teaspoon of sugar each time
✔ Stir each container of sugar the same number of times.
✔ Make sure the water is the same temperature each time
✔ Always use the same kind of sugar
✔ Use different amounts of water

Q2: Do the experiment — ignore it at your peril.

Q3:

Amount of water	100ml	200ml	300ml	400ml
Time it takes to dissolve (in seconds)	40 s	35 s	30 s	25 s

(using spare results)

Q4: When there was 100ml of water, the sugar took **MORE** time to dissolve **THAN** when there was 400ml of water. The time it takes to dissolve sugar **DECREASES** if there is more water. The time it takes sugar to dissolve **DEPENDS** on how much water there is.

Page 15 Stirring and Dissolving

Q1: a) Stir each container the same number of times.
Use different amounts of water.
b) You should stir each container a different number of times, while using the same amount of water each time.

Q2:

Number of stirs	5	10	15	20
Time it takes to dissolve (in seconds)	51 s	39 s	27 s	15 s

(using spare results)

Q3: When I stirred the sugar 5 times, it dissolved **MORE SLOWLY THAN** when I stirred it 20 times. If you stir the sugar more times, the sugar dissolves more **QUICKLY**. Stirring the sugar is a **GOOD** way to speed up dissolving.

Page 16 Type of Sugar and Dissolving

Q1: Use exactly one flat teaspoon of sugar each time.
Stir each container of sugar the same number of times.
Make sure the water is the same temperature each time.
Use the same amount of water each time.

Q2: Do the experiment — or the world will collapse.

Q3:

Type of sugar	Caster 1st time	Granulated 1st time	Caster 2nd time	Granulated 2nd time
Time it takes to dissolve (in seconds)	15 s	36 s	17 s	37 s

(using spare results)

Q4: When I used caster sugar, the sugar dissolved more **QUICKLY** than when I used granulated sugar. The granulated sugar took **MORE** time to dissolve. Using **CASTER** sugar is a good way to speed up dissolving.

Dissolving Faster

This mini-project is all about how you can speed up dissolving.
You have to find out <u>what</u> things affect the speed of dissolving and <u>how</u> they affect it.

Q1 It's important that you do a fair test. What is a fair test? Tick ✔ the sentence that's true.

A fair test is when you do the test in fine weather. ☐

A fair test is when everyone gets a turn to do the experiment, so nobody's left out. ☐

A fair test is when only one thing gets changed, so you know that if the results are different, it's because of the thing that's been changed. ☐

A fair test is when you use the same amount of sugar each time. ☐

...and then I cheated and ruined his fair test.

Derek was about to throw a wobbly with the sugar cubes.

If you want it to be a fair test (which you do), you have to <u>find out</u> what kind of things could affect how quickly something dissolves. That way, you can make sure only <u>one</u> of them gets changed.

Q2 Have a butcher's (that's cockney rhyming slang for 'look', because it rhymes with 'butcher's hook') at these sentences. Write out the ones that could affect how quickly sugar dissolves.

How much sugar there is in the water.

Whether you like eating sugar.

How many times you stir the sugar, and how vigorously.

Whether you use fine or coarse sugar.

How much water there is.

What shape the container is.

Whether you've already done the experiment with salt instead.

What temperature the water is.

How sloping the table is.

How much water there is. ⟵ I did this one for you as a special favour.

....

....

....

....

....

This is the sweetest experiment I've done...

This experiment's a doddle, but you still have to be real <u>careful</u> to get accurate results. Make it a <u>fair test</u> and you should have no problems, unless a little donkey eats all your sugar.

MINI-PROJECT

Water Volume and Dissolving

The first thing to test is whether or not the <u>volume of water</u> affects how quickly the sugar dissolves.

Q1 Here are some ways of doing the experiment. Tick the sentence from each pair that would be a <u>better</u> idea.

Use exactly one flat teaspoon of sugar each time. ☐   OR   Use any amount of sugar. ☐

Stir each container of sugar the same number of times. ☐   OR   Stir each container of sugar a different number of times. ☐

Put some of the sugar in hot water and some in cold water. ☐   OR   Make sure the water is the same temperature each time. ☐

Use caster sugar and granulated sugar. ☐   OR   Always use the same kind of sugar. ☐

Use the same amount of water each time. ☐   OR   Use different amounts of water. ☐

Q2 Follow these instructions to do the experiment. Make sure you do all the things you said were good ideas in Q1. (If you can't do the experiment, use my spare results at the bottom of the page.)

> Using a measuring jug, measure out 100 ml of water into a container. Put the sugar in the water, stir it 10 times and time how long it takes the sugar to dissolve completely. Write the time down. Do the same thing with 200 ml, 300 ml and 400 ml of water.

Q3 Write down your results in this table.

Use <u>warm</u>, but <u>not boiling</u> water — or you might get scalded.

Amount of water	100ml	200ml	300ml	400ml
Time it takes to dissolve (in seconds)				

Q4 Circle the right words and cross out the wrong words in this sentence.

When there was 100 ml of water, the sugar took MORE / LESS / THE SAME time to

dissolve THAN / AS when there was 400 ml of water. The time it takes to dissolve

sugar INCREASES / DECREASES / STAYS THE SAME if there is more water. The time it

takes sugar to dissolve DEPENDS / DOESN'T DEPEND on how much water there is.

Spare results: 100 ml: 40 s. 200 ml: 35 s. 300 ml: 30 s. 400 ml: 25 s.

<u>Change the volume — I like it loud...</u>

It's important that you do all the things in Question 1 that make it a <u>fair test</u>. And using <u>warm</u> water helps, but make sure it isn't <u>too hot</u> — because that would really hurt if you splashed yourself.

Stirring and Dissolving

The fun continues — this time, the thing you're going to vary is the number of <u>stirs</u> you give the sugar.

Q1 a) In Q1 on the last page, you ticked things you should do to make the experiment a fair test. Write down two things you said last time that you definitely should <u>not</u> do this time.

....

....

b) What two things should you do that you DIDN'T do last time?

....

....

Stir-fry anyone?

Wrong stirring test — Wok a terrible mistake to make.

Q2 Just like last time, get four containers and follow the instructions below, remembering to do all the things that make it a fair test. Warm water is best (but not boiling).

Put some sugar in a container of water. Stir the sugar 5 times and time how long it takes for the sugar to dissolve (from the time you start stirring). Write down the time. Do the same with 10 stirs, 15 stirs and 20 stirs. Write your results in the table below.

IMPORTANT — you must stir in the <u>same way</u> each time. So make really sure your stirs don't get <u>faster</u> or <u>longer</u>, or it won't be a fair test.

(If you can't do the experiment, use the spare results at the bottom of the page.)

Number of stirs	5	10	15	20
Time it takes to dissolve (in seconds)				

Q3 Choose the right words from the brackets to complete these sentences.

When I stirred the sugar 5 times, it dissolved FASTER THAN / MORE SLOWLY THAN / AT THE SAME SPEED AS when I stirred it 20 times. If you stir the sugar more times, the sugar dissolves more QUICKLY / SLOWLY / STRANGELY. Stirring the sugar is a GOOD / BAD way to speed up dissolving.

Spare results: 5 stirs: 51 s. 10 stirs: 39 s. 15 stirs: 27 s. 20 stirs: 15 s.

A great experiment — it's stirring stuff...

This experiment isn't hard — make sure you use the <u>same</u> amount of sugar each time, and don't change the way you <u>stir</u>. Don't panic if you think you've done it wrong — just do it <u>again</u> to <u>check</u>.

MINI-PROJECT

Type of Sugar and Dissolving

You've guessed it — here's an experiment to investigate <u>another</u> thing that might affect the speed of dissolving. This time it's the <u>type of sugar</u>.

Q1 Write out all the important things you'll need to do this time to make the experiment work — you can look back at the last two pages for ideas. I've written down the first one for you, because it's different from before.

Use caster sugar and granulated sugar.

....

....

....

....

....

Sharon preferred icing sugar.

Q2 Follow these instructions to do the experiment. Do the things from Q1, and use warm water.

Get four containers and put the same amount of water in each. Put <u>caster</u> sugar in the first one, stir it 10 times, and time how long it takes to dissolve completely. In the next container, put the same amount of <u>granulated</u> sugar, and do the same thing. Do the experiment again with the other two containers (to check that your results weren't mucked up).

Caster sugar is more finely ground than granulated sugar — so the bits are smaller.

Q3 Put your results in this table. (Or use my spare results at the bottom of the page.)

Type of sugar	Caster (1st time)	Granulated (1st time)	Caster (2nd time)	Granulated (2nd time)
Time it takes to dissolve (in seconds)				

Q4 Now for the conclusion. Fill in the gaps in these sentences.

When I used caster sugar, the sugar dissolved more .... than when

I used granulated sugar. The granulated sugar took .... time to

dissolve. Using .... sugar is a good way to speed up dissolving.

Spare results: Caster: 15 s, 17 s. Granulated: 36 s, 37 s.

What sugar do old ladies like? — Gran-ulated...

Do this experiment in exactly the same way as the other two, and you'll be <u>fine</u>. It's useful to do it in <u>pairs</u> so that one person can stir while the other times how long it takes to dissolve.

Graph City

MINI-PROJECT

Graphs are great. So are bar charts. They show you really easily
how the speed of dissolving is affected by different things.

Q1   Draw a line graph of the results you got for the experiment on page 14 on this graph paper:

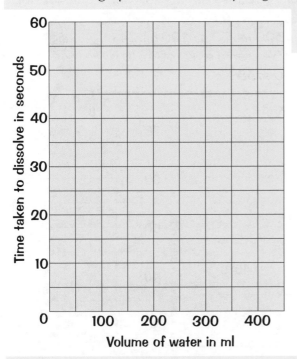

Which is easier to read and understand —
the table of results or the graph?

....

Time taken to dissolve in seconds (y-axis: 10, 20, 30, 40, 50, 60)
Volume of water in ml (x-axis: 0, 100, 200, 300, 400)

No!

Drinking the evidence before the sugar
dissolved was Marvin's big mistake.

Q2   Put the results of the stirring experiment on page 15 into a line graph (on the left).
Put the results of the type of sugar experiment on page 16 into a bar chart (on the right).

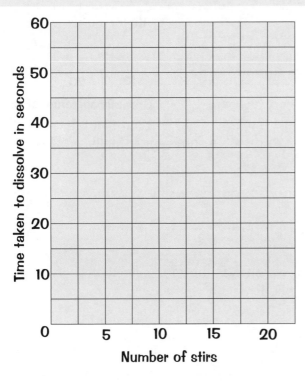

Time taken to dissolve in seconds (y-axis: 10, 20, 30, 40, 50, 60)
Number of stirs (x-axis: 0, 5, 10, 15, 20)

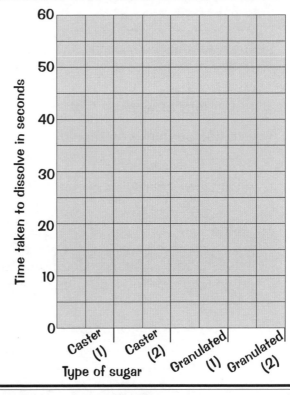

Time taken to dissolve in seconds (y-axis: 10, 20, 30, 40, 50, 60)
Type of sugar (x-axis: Caster (1), Caster (2), Granulated (1), Granulated (2))

Top of the fruit charts — lime graph...

For the first two experiments, a line graph is useful — but for the third one (type of sugar),
a bar chart is better. Read your results carefully and make extra sure you plot them right.

MINI-PROJECT

Graph City

Q1 I did the three experiments from the last pages, and wrote down my results. Add them to your graphs on page 17, in a different colour. Are they similar to your results or not?

> Amount of water — 100 ml: 42 s. 200 ml: 36 s. 300 ml: 30 s. 400 ml: 24 s.
> Number of stirs — 5 stirs: 55 s. 10 stirs: 42 s. 15 stirs: 31 s. 20 stirs: 18 s.
> Type of sugar — Caster: 14 s, 13 s. Granulated: 40 s, 38 s.

Small Paul had trouble with graphs.

These results ARE / ARE NOT similar to my results.

Q2 I did an experiment to find out whether the <u>temperature</u> of the water affected how quickly the sugar dissolved. I wrote my results in this table. Draw a line graph of the results on the graph paper.

Temperature of water	10°C	20°C	30°C	40°C
Time it takes to dissolve (in seconds)	70 s	55 s	40 s	25 s

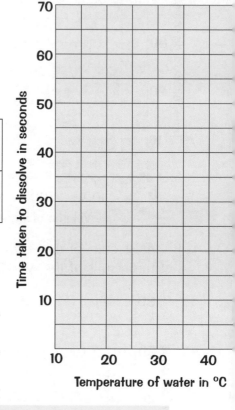

Q3 Does temperature affect the speed of dissolving? How?

....

....

....

Q4 What do you think you should do if you want to dissolve some sugar <u>really</u> quickly?

....

....

Q5 Out of the things that speeded up dissolving, which was the <u>most</u> effective? And which made the <u>least</u> difference to the speed?

....

....

All this dissolving is making me weaker and

Knowing how to speed up dissolving is useful if you're making a sugary drink in a rush. But it's even <u>more</u> useful to know the stuff about <u>fair tests</u> and putting your <u>results</u> in graphs and tables.

Repeating Measurements

It'd be a bit of a fluke if you got <u>exactly</u> the same results for an experiment every time you did it.
To be <u>really sure</u> they're as right as you can make them, you need to <u>repeat</u> the experiment.

ACE Products have invented a new kind of artificial sweetener. They want to know
how long one sweetener takes to dissolve in water at different temperatures.

Roger, Hilary and Louise from ACE Laboratory are testing the sweeteners.
They are dissolving one sweetener in 200 ml of water at different temperatures.

Actual size

Q1   Put each person's results on the graph.
Draw a cross for each point.
(You don't need to draw a line through them yet.)

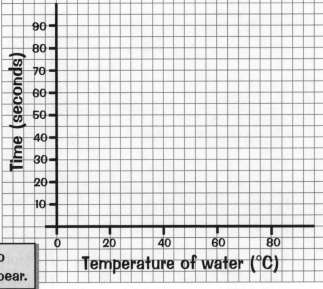

Name: *Roger*	
Temperature of water	Time (seconds)
20 °C	75
40 °C	60
60 °C	30
80 °C	15

Name: *Hilary*	
Temperature of water	Time (seconds)
20 °C	70
40 °C	50
60 °C	35
80 °C	20

Name: *Louise*	
Temperature of water	Time (seconds)
20 °C	85
40 °C	60
60 °C	40
80 °C	15

Professor Bighair tried to artificially sweeten a nasty bear.

Q2 a)   Are the results for 80 °C spread out or close together? ....

b)   Are the results for 20 °C spread out or close together? ....

Q3 a)   Which temperature has results that you would trust the <u>most</u>? ....

b)   Which temperature has results that you would trust the <u>least</u>? ....

When your results are a bit scattered,
you need to draw a <u>line</u> that
goes roughly through the
<u>middle</u> of the points.

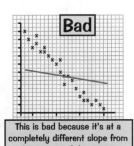

Bad

This is bad because it just goes through the <u>highest</u> points. Most points are <u>below</u> the line.

Good

This is good because it goes through the middle of the points, and there's roughly the same number of points on either side of the line.

Bad

This is bad because it's at a completely different slope from the pattern of the points.

Q4   Draw a line on the graph in Q1. Make sure it goes through the middle of the points.

Take an exam twice — improve your results...

There'd be no point doing an experiment if you didn't know whether your results were any good.
That's why you <u>repeat</u> the measurements — if they're the <u>same</u>, you know you're pretty much <u>right</u>.

Drawing a Good Line on Your Graphs

A great graph needs a <u>line</u> on it to show the results properly.
The line shows the pattern of the results and you can use it to make a <u>conclusion</u>.

Milky Products, who make Mr Milky's Milkshake Mix, have had a few complaints. Some customers think it doesn't dissolve properly. Four people from ACE Laboratory are testing <u>how long</u> it takes <u>different amounts</u> of Milkshake Mix to dissolve in 500 ml of milk.

Q1 Use a different coloured cross to put each person's results on the graph paper. Fill in the key under the graph. (You don't need to draw a line on the graph yet.)

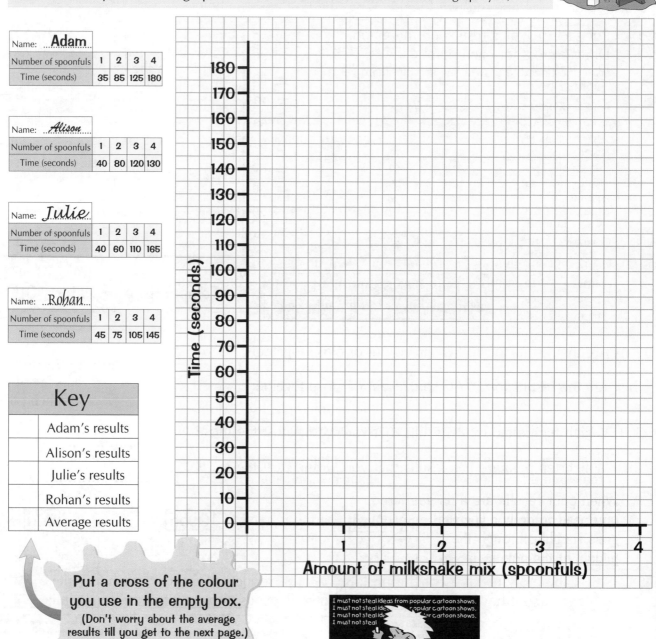

Name: **Adam**

Number of spoonfuls	1	2	3	4
Time (seconds)	35	85	125	180

Name: *Alison*

Number of spoonfuls	1	2	3	4
Time (seconds)	40	80	120	130

Name: *Julie*

Number of spoonfuls	1	2	3	4
Time (seconds)	40	60	110	165

Name: *Rohan*

Number of spoonfuls	1	2	3	4
Time (seconds)	45	75	105	145

Key	
	Adam's results
	Alison's results
	Julie's results
	Rohan's results
	Average results

Put a cross of the colour you use in the empty box.
(Don't worry about the average results till you get to the next page.)

I must not steal ideas from popular cartoon shows.
I must not steal ide... popular cartoon shows.
I must not steal id... ar cartoon shows.
I must not steal

Bart's teacher always made him do lines.

Actors can't do graphs — they forget the lines...

The line you draw is the finishing touch to a graph. It should go right through the <u>middle</u> of the points and have roughly the <u>same number</u> of points on each side. Anything else would just be rubbish.

Drawing a Good Line on Your Graphs

You need to look back at the graph on the last page to answer these questions.

Q1a) Which amount of milkshake mix gave results that you trust <u>most</u>? ....

b) Which amount of milkshake mix gave results that you trust <u>least</u>? ....

Q2 When you've got scattered points on your graph, <u>where</u> should you draw the line through them? (Ring) the best answers below.

So that the line goes through the highest points.

So that the line goes straight across through the lowest point.

So that the slope of the line roughly shows the pattern of the results.

So there are roughly as many points above the line as below it.

So that the line goes through the lowest points.

Jane had scattered <u>milkshake</u> all over her graph.

Q3 Draw a line on your graph (on the last page) that follows the pattern of the crosses well.

Q4 a) Work out the average results and put them in this table. Put these points on the graph using a new colour, and add that colour to the key.

Number of spoonfuls	1	2	3	4
Average Time (seconds)	....	....	....	....

To work out the average, add up the 4 results and then divide by 4.

b) Draw a line through the points for the average results. Compare it to your first line and circle the answer below that best sums it up.

The average line is about the <u>same</u> as my line.

The average line is <u>higher</u> than my line.

The average line is <u>lower</u> than my line.

c) Is the average line a good representation of the results? (Circle) YES or NO. YES NO

Q5 ACE Laboratory needs a conclusion to tell Milky Products. Use your graph to write a sentence about how <u>length of time to dissolve</u> depends on <u>amount of milkshake mix</u>.

....

....

Learning to draw graphs — it's all in the line of duty...

If you <u>repeat</u> measurements loads of times, the average results will represent the data well. Then you can make a conclusion and be <u>absolutely certain</u> that it's right. Smug grins all round.

Making a Good Conclusion

Every experiment needs results you can be sure about.

No one is buying Mr Milky's Milkshake Mix because it doesn't dissolve properly.
ACE Laboratory thinks the secret might be to use hot milk instead of cold milk.
Four people did a test and their results are shown in the graph below.

Q1 There are three lines drawn on this graph. One is a much better line than the other two. Decide how well each line represents the results. Circle GOOD or BAD and say why.

Green line GOOD BAD

....

....

Red line GOOD BAD

....

....

Blue line GOOD BAD

....

....

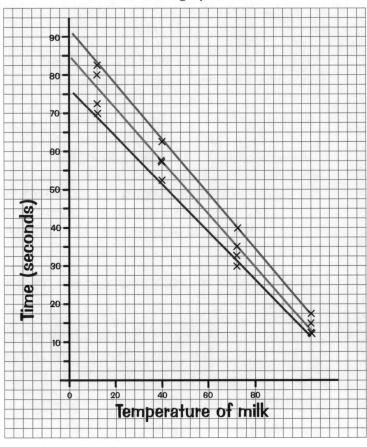

Q2 Use the graph to write a conclusion about how the length of time it takes to dissolve depends on the temperature of the milk.

....

....

Q3 Why is it useful to repeat results?
Hint: Would Milky Products believe these results?

The Milkshake Mix just wasn't hot enough.

....

....

So what's the conclusion? — Well, it's a happy one...

Milky Products had confidence in the results on this graph. They changed the instructions on the packet to say 'add to hot milk'. And everyone slurped lovely milkshake happily ever after.

Revision Questions

I know you've really enjoyed this book — so now you can relive it __all over again__ for practice...

Q1 I'm not sure which of my ingredients will dissolve in the hot water when I make soup. Tick the ones that will dissolve, and put a cross next to the ones which won't dissolve.

Banana   Salt   Sugar cubes   Pepper   Potatoes

Q2 Susan has dropped her gravel collection and her dust collection into a hat full of water by mistake. There are big bits of gravel and tiny dusty bits. How can Susan separate the gravel, dust and water again?   [Clue: she needs to do 2 different things.]

1) ....

....

2) ....

....

Q3 Martin left a mug of salty water on a shelf. After 3 weeks he noticed the water had gone and there was a hard white solid at the bottom. Circle the right words to explain what happened.

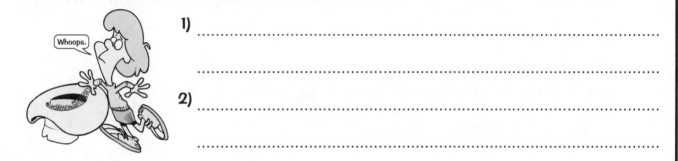

When you leave a solution of a liquid and a solid for a long time, only

the LIQUID / SOLID evaporates off. That means that when all the

LIQUID / SOLID has gone, there's only the LIQUID / SOLID left.

Q4 Draw in the method in the box, then put a tick next to the correct sentence on the right.

Making the solution   Filtering the solution   Tasting the solution

I can still taste coffee...

The coffee powder...

stays in the solution.

is filtered out.

__Salty water — it brings tears to your eyes...__

I know it's a bit of a pain having to trudge through these kinds of questions all over again, just when you thought you'd finished the topic — but practice makes __perfect__ and soon you'll be a __pro__.

Revision Questions

They think it's all over... but it's not. The end is in sight, though. You can do it...

Q1 Fill in the gaps in this paragraph using words from the beaker.

When you make a solution, you put a solid into some water.

It .... by breaking up into tiny pieces

that are .... than the holes in a piece

of .... paper.

If you heat up the solution, the water evaporates, but the pieces of

solid can't .... so they're left behind. That means that the steam

only contains .... and not the ....

Beaker words: DISSOLVES, EVAPORATE, SMALLER, NEWS, LARGER, SOLID, WATER, FILTER

Q2 Luke Warm is heating up some red ink with his laser eyesight, and he's collecting and condensing the steam. Will the condensed steam be red?

....

If not, why not? Where is the redness?

....

....

Cold surface

Q3 I've made a graph of my results from an experiment and now I want to draw a line that follows the pattern of the crosses. Write 'GOOD' or 'BAD' under each of these attempts.

....

It's not over till the fat lady evaporates...

Ho-hum, these questions keep on coming. I know you love them really. Don't rush through them just because you've nearly finished the book though — take your time and savour each question.

Revision Questions

Last page of the book — I'd better make it extra tricky.

Q1 Fill in this table by saying whether each statement is 'TRUE' or 'FALSE', and then write a way of testing each statement.

Statement	True or False?	How could you test it?
When you evaporate sweetened tea, the sugar will evaporate with the water.		
Salt will dissolve quicker in hot water than in cold water.		
Chalk will dissolve in water.		
It makes a difference whether you stir clockwise or anti-clockwise.		
Bath salts dissolve quicker when you stir the water.		

Q2 Just do this crossword — and then you're finished.

Clues — Down:

1) A good method for separating dust from water.
2) A mix of water and a dissolved solid.
4) Steam only consists of this.
5) A good line on a graph should have roughly the ---- number of points on either side.

Clues — Across:

3) If you put salt into water, it will -------- .
5) This is good for removing big lumps from a liquid.
6) When water is heated, it evaporates as -----.
7) A ---- test is when you change only one thing at a time.

That's it — I think my brain's dissolved...

I can't believe there's another 10 pages of questions... only kidding. That's your lot about dissolving. Unless this book's so popular that we write "Even More About Dissolving". You never know...

Index